ART NOUVEAU
DESIGNS
COLORING BOOK

MARTY NOBLE

DOVER PUBLICATIONS, INC.
MINEOLA, NEW YORK

Bibliographical Note

Art Nouveau Designs Coloring Book contains all the plates from the following previously published Dover books by Marty Noble: *Art Nouveau Animal Designs* and *Art Nouveau Patterns*.

This 2014 edition printed for Barnes & Noble, Inc., by Dover Publications, Inc.

International Standard Book Number
ISBN-13: 978-1-4351-5845-0

Manufactured in the United States by Courier Corporation

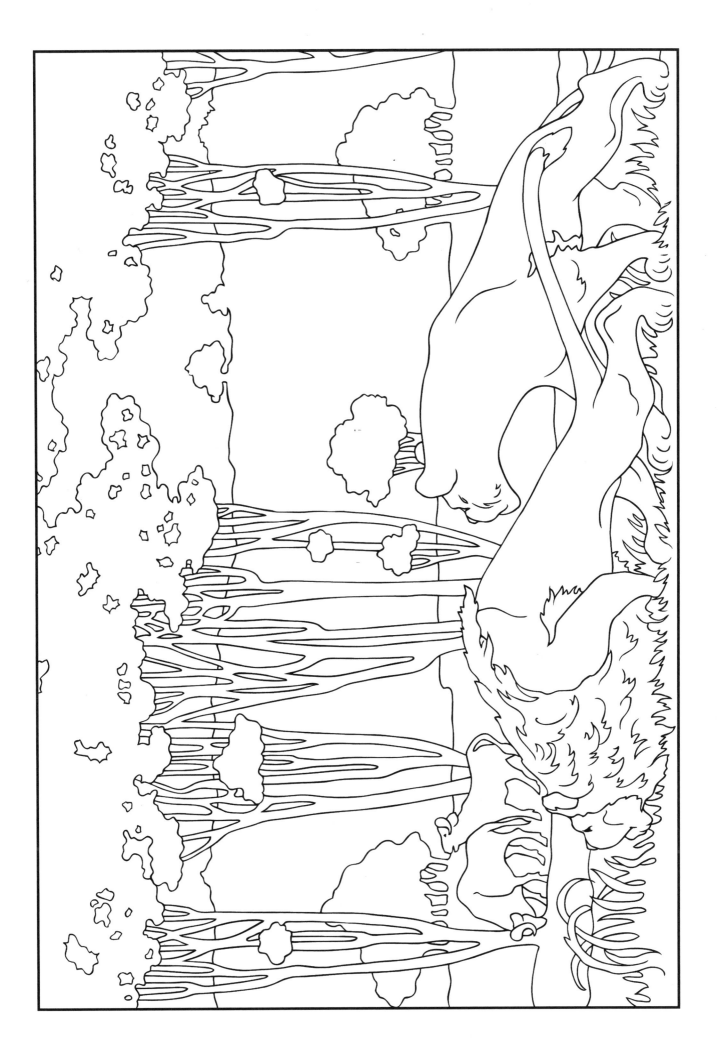

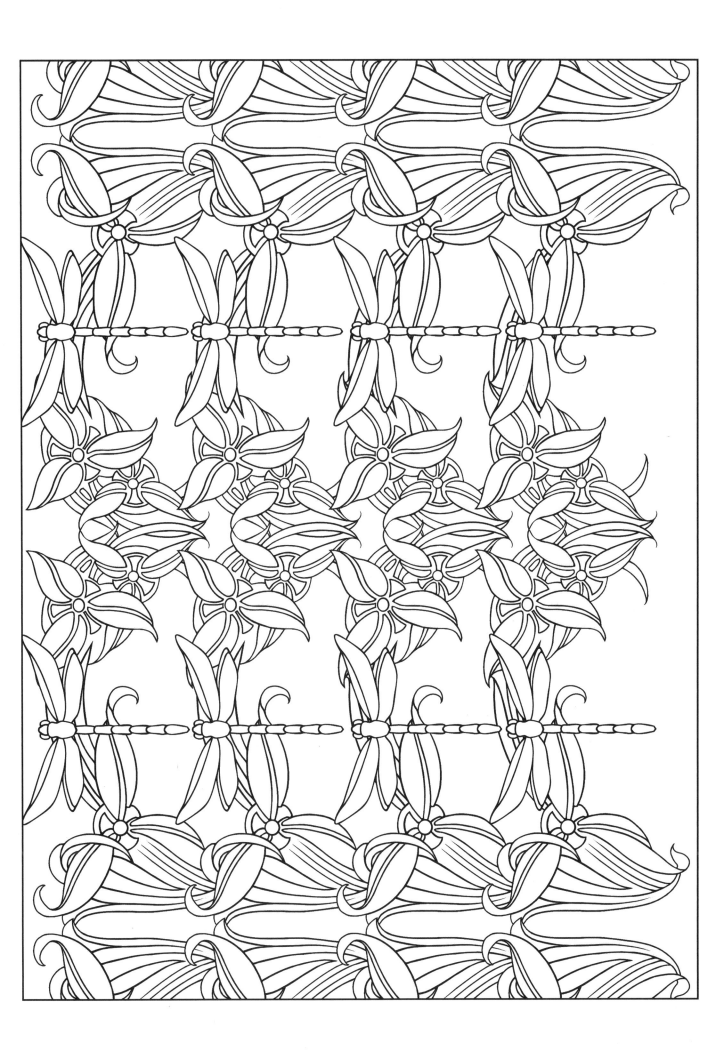

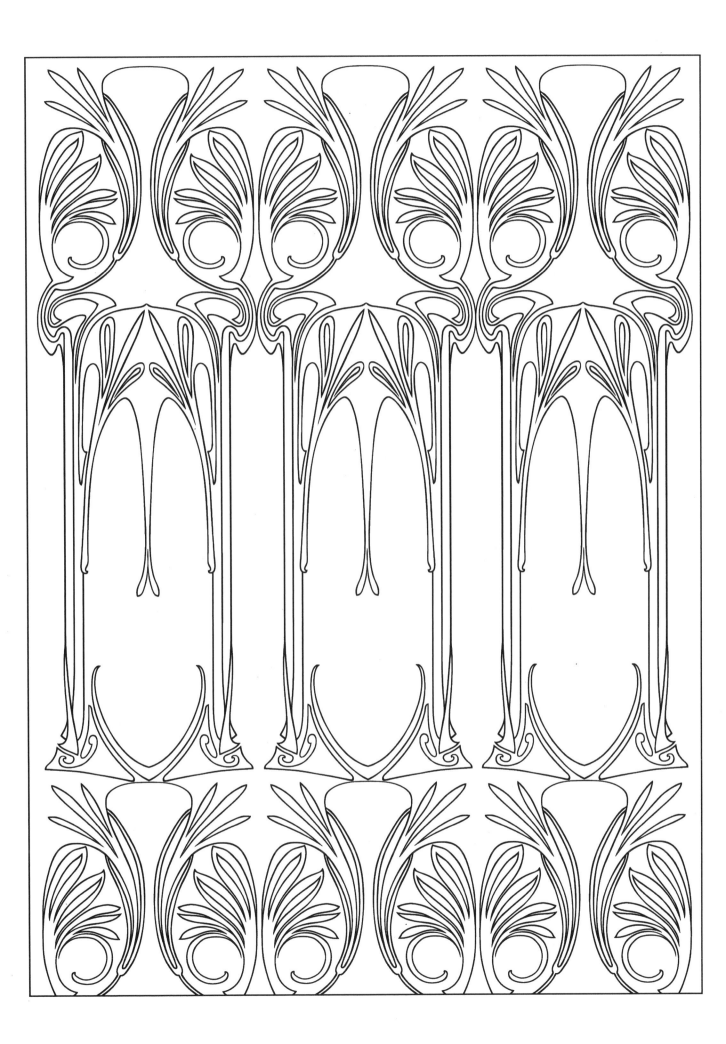